Forward Thinking
A WELLBEING, HAPPINESS & FULFILMENT JOURNAL

Drawing on fascinating and heart warming research into wellbeing, fulfilment and happiness, **Forward Thinking** offers ideas and suggested mindful activities to help you be in your element.

Explore and record your journey of self discovery, your hopes, plans and achievements and live the life you wish to lead.

Peter Coxon is a consultant psychologist focussing on personal and leadership development. He maintains a healthy life balance working with interesting organisations, coaching leaders, business and sporting teams plus keeping fit, having fun and spending quality time with family and friends.

JOURNALS® of a LIFETIME
made with love *from you to me*
www.JournalsOfALifetime.com

NAME:

....

ADDRESS:

....

....

....

....

PHONE NUMBER:

....

EMAIL:

....

Forward Thinking
A WELLBEING, HAPPINESS & FULFILMENT JOURNAL

Forward Thinking is a journal with a difference. Using leading edge research on wellbeing, happiness and fulfilment, it is designed to help promote positive thinking and focus your view on life.

Many people believe they will be happy and feel fulfilled when they are rich, married, promoted, etc. However, all the external factors in our lives will only account for 10% of the variance of our happiness, some 50% is determined by our genetics which can be challenging, but not impossible to increase.

The good news is that the remaining 40% of our happiness can be relatively easily influenced by our intentional activities, how we think and how we behave.

(The How of Happiness - A practical guide to getting the life you want- Sonja Lyubomirsky 2011)

This journal focusses on the 40% and by increasing this it may, in turn, positively influence the 50%. After completing some generic positioning questionnaires, there are 52 weekly mindfulness activities to encourage you to be Forward Thinking, to engage your intentional activities and to raise your happiness set point.

THE LAST YEAR

Spend a little time reflecting on the
positive from the past 12 months.

What were you pleased about?

....
....
....
....
....
....
....
....

What sparked your interest?

....
....
....
....
....
....
....
....

What inspired you?

What gave you real satisfaction?

What strengthened your friendships / relationships?

....
....
....
....
....
....
....
....
....

What gave you joy?

....
....
....
....
....
....
....
....
....

REFLECTION QUESTIONS

Measure your own sense of well being by reflecting on:

RELATIONSHIPS:

How satisfied are you with your close relationships?

....

....

....

....

....

....

....

HEALTH, FITNESS & WELLBEING:

How is your health, fitness & wellbeing?

....

....

....

....

....

....

....

JOB SATISFACTION:

How would you describe your job satisfaction?

....

....

....

....

....

....

....

....

PERSONAL ACTIVITIES:

What personal activities (including volunteering) are you engaged in?

....

....

....

....

....

....

....

....

FINANCES:

How secure are you economically? How stable is your income?

....

....

....

....

....

....

....

....

COMMUNITY:

How involved have you been in local/community events & issues?

....

....

....

....

....

....

....

....

FINDING YOUR CURRENT HAPPINESS 'SET POINT'

Most people's happiness tends not to change significantly through their lives. Major life changing events tend to have short term impacts, yet within 2 years or so most people return to their 'set point'.

The good news is that we can work on ourselves to cultivate attitudes and behaviours that promote our own happiness and wellbeing and improve our set point.

Using the Oxford happiness questionnaire, the first exercise will gauge your own set point!

This journal has a range of suggested activities, to aid a change in perspective. By undertaking them on a weekly basis you can create habits that will change your outlook and increase your 'set point'. Try a number of them and with some self discipline you can select and make habits of your own favourite tasks that work best for you.

Good luck . . .

and some of these ideas may help you make your own luck.

The Oxford Happiness Questionnaire and Happiness Activities Fit exercise are reproduced with permission from The How of Happiness: The Practical Guide to Getting the Life You Want. Sonja Lyubomirssky pub: Piaitkius

THE OXFORD HAPPINESS QUESTIONNAIRE

Assessing your own 'set point'

Below are a number of statements about happiness. Using a pencil indicate how much you agree or disagree with each statement by entering a number alongside it according to the scale below.

1	2	3	4	5	6
Strongly disagree	Moderately disagree	Slightly disagree	Slightly agree	Moderately agree	Strongly agree

STATEMENT: SCORE:

1	I don't feel particularly pleased with the way I am	....	R
2	I am intensely interested in other people	....	
3	I feel that life is very rewarding	....	
4	I have very warm feelings towards almost everyone	....	
5	I rarely wake up feeling rested	....	R
6	I'm not particularly optimistic about the future	....	R
7	I find most things amusing	....	

8	I am always committed and involved	....
9	Life is good	....
10	I don't think that the world is a good place	....	R
11	I laugh a lot	....
12	I am well satisfied with everything in my life	....
13	I don't think I look attractive	....	R
14	There's a gap between what I would like to do and what I have done	....	R
15	I am very happy	....
16	I find beauty in some things	....
17	I always have a cheerful effect on others	....
18	I can find time for everything I want to	....

1	2	3	4	5	6
Strongly disagree	Moderately disagree	Slightly disagree	Slightly agree	Moderately agree	Strongly agree

19	I feel that I'm not especially in control of my life	....	R
20	I feel able to take anything on	....	
21	I feel fully mentally alert	....	
22.	I often experience joy and elation	....	
23	I don't find it easy to make decisions	....	R
24	I don't have a particular sense of meaning and purpose in my life	....	R
25	I feel I have a great deal of energy	....	
26	I usually have a positive influence on events	....	
27	I don't have fun with other people	....	R
28	I don't feel particularly healthy	....	R
29	I don't have particularly happy memories of the past	....	R

HOW TO CALCULATE YOUR SCORE

STEP 1

Your scores on the 12 items marked with an R should be 'reverse-scored' - that is, if you gave yourself a 1, rub it out and change it to a 6; if you gave yourself a 2, change that to a 5; change 4 to a 3; change a 5 to a 2; and change a 6 to a 1.

STEP 2

Using the changed scores for those 12 items,
now add the scores for all the 29 statements.

STEP 3

Happiness 'set point' = Total (from Step 2) divided by 29

Your current happiness 'set point' is:

....

WHAT IT MEANS

Research behind The Oxford Happiness Questionnaire (Hills and Argyle 2002) suggests that we will typically vary no more than +or– 2 points from our 'set point' through life due to events which may raise or lower our 'set point' temporarily, but we are likely to revert to our 'set point' over time.

Your score is 'your score' and can't be compared with others. There is no right or wrong score, but it represents a point in time from which you can move. By working on our outlook and developing some self discipline in our thinking and our behaviour, this score can be increased and maintained at that higher position. This journal aims to raise your set point by working on positive thinking and attitudes. It takes some discipline so believe in yourself.

HOW TO FIND HAPPINESS ACTIVITIES THAT FIT

Consider each of the following 12 happiness activities. Reflect on what it would be like to do it every week for a long period of time. People do things for many different reasons. Rate why you might keep doing this activity in terms of each of the following reasons.

NATURAL: I'll keep doing this activity because it will feel 'natural' to me and I'll be able to stick with it.

ENJOY: I'll keep doing this activity because I will enjoy doing it: I'll find it to be interesting and challenging.

VALUE: I'll keep doing this activity because I will value and identify with doing it; I'll do it freely even when it's not enjoyable.

GUILTY: I'll keep doing this activity because I would feel ashamed, guilty or anxious if I don't do it; I'll force myself.

SITUATION: I'll keep doing this activity because somebody else will want me to, or because my situation will force me to.

Adapted from Ken Sheldon's 'Person activity fit diagnostic' cited in 'The How of Happiness.'

1. Expressing gratitude: Counting your blessings for what you have (privately or to others), or conveying your gratitude and appreciation to people whom you've never properly thanked.

NATURAL	ENJOY	VALUE	GUILTY	SITUATION
☐	☐	☐	☐	☐

2. Cultivating optimism: Keeping a journal in which you imagine and write about the best possible future for yourself, or practise looking at the bright side of every situation. *

NATURAL	ENJOY	VALUE	GUILTY	SITUATION
☐	☐	☐	☐	☐

3. Avoiding over-thinking and social comparison: Using strategies (such as distraction) to cut down on how often you dwell on your problems and compare yourself to others.

NATURAL	ENJOY	VALUE	GUILTY	SITUATION
☐	☐	☐	☐	☐

4. Practising acts of kindness: Doing good things for others, whether friends or strangers, either directly or anonymously, either spontaneously or planned.

NATURAL	ENJOY	VALUE	GUILTY	SITUATION
☐	☐	☐	☐	☐

5. Nurturing relationships: Picking a relationship in need of strengthening, and investing time and energy in healing, cultivating, affirming and enjoying it.

NATURAL   ENJOY   VALUE   GUILTY   SITUATION

☐   ☐   ☐   ☐   ☐

6. Developing strategies for coping: Practising ways to endure or surmount a recent stress, hardship or trauma.

NATURAL   ENJOY   VALUE   GUILTY   SITUATION

☐   ☐   ☐   ☐   ☐

7. Learning to forgive: Keeping a journal or writing a letter in which you work on letting go of anger and resentment towards one or more individuals who have hurt or wronged you.

NATURAL   ENJOY   VALUE   GUILTY   SITUATION

☐   ☐   ☐   ☐   ☐

8. Doing more activities that truly engage you: Increasing the number of experiences at home and work in which you 'lose' yourself, which are challenging and absorbing.

NATURAL   ENJOY   VALUE   GUILTY   SITUATION

☐   ☐   ☐   ☐   ☐

9. Savouring life's joys: Paying close attention, taking delight and replaying life's momentary pleasures and wonders - through thinking, writing, drawing or sharing with another.

NATURAL ☐   ENJOY ☐   VALUE ☐   GUILTY ☐   SITUATION ☐

10. Committing to your goals: Picking one, two or three significant goals that are meaningful to you and devoting time and effort to pursuing them.

NATURAL ☐   ENJOY ☐   VALUE ☐   GUILTY ☐   SITUATION ☐

11. Practising spirituality: Becoming more involved in reading and pondering spiritually themed books.

NATURAL ☐   ENJOY ☐   VALUE ☐   GUILTY ☐   SITUATION ☐

12. Taking care of your body: Engaging in physical activity, meditating, smiling and laughing.

NATURAL ☐   ENJOY ☐   VALUE ☐   GUILTY ☐   SITUATION ☐

LOOKING FORWARD

What's next? What is it you plan to do?

Shade in your wheel according to how well you are fairing so far
against each life segment. The more you shade the happier you feel.
The picture that emerges will suggest where you are comfortable with
your life and where it may be out of balance and what aspects of life
you may wish to address.

Imagine a happy and fulfilling future.
What would you like to achieve in the next 6 month to
create a long term sense of well-being?

RELATIONSHIPS:

What might you do to maintain or improve them?

....

....

....

....

HEALTH, FITNESS & WELLBEING:

What might you wish to do to maintain or improve it?

....

....

....

....

COMMUNITY:

How might you be more involved in local/community events & issues?

....

....

....

....

JOB SATISFACTION:

How might you develop this during the year ahead?

....

....

....

....

....

FINANCES:

What might you need to focus on?

....

....

....

....

....

PERSONAL ACTIVITIES:

What would you like to pursue or develop this year?

....

....

....

....

....

We have time for anything, but not everything. You have to decide your priorities. Tick the three segments you'd most like to focus on.

RELATIONSHIPS	PERSONAL ACTIVITIES

HEALTH, FITNESS & WELLBEING	FINANCES

JOB SATISFACTION	COMMUNITY

"Happiness is not about what happens to you, but how you choose to respond to what happens."

KAREN SALMONSOHN

Week Starting : _____

Record something to look forward to this week.
Remind yourself not of what is urgent, but of what is important.
Make notes on how it went and what you enjoyed.

"Good relationships give us a sense of well being and happiness."

UNKNOWN

Week Starting : _____

Write a short letter to someone you love, describing the impact they
have on you and how much you care for them.

....

....

....

....

....

....

....

....

....

....

....

....

....

....

....

....

....

....

....

"Make sure the goals you are setting are SMART: Specific, Measurable, Achievable, Relevant and Timely."

GEORGE DORAN

Week Starting : _____

Setting achievable goals each week and reflecting on them creates
habits. Set some SMART goals and at the end of each day write down
what you achieved that made you happy.

MON:
....
....

TUES:
....
....

WEDS:
....
....

THURS:
....
....

FRI:
....
....

SAT:
....
....

SUN:
....
....

"Life can only
be understood
backwards; but
it must be lived
forwards."

SOREN KIERKEGAARD

Think about some of the most wonderful experiences in your
life so far. Choose one to relive in your mind.
Write down what happened and how it felt.

....

....

....

....

....

....

....

....

....

....

....

....

....

....

....

....

....

....

....

....

"The power of finding beauty in the humblest thing makes home happy and life lovely."

LOUISA MAY ALCOTT

Week Starting : _____

All week look around your surroundings, your home, while you
travel, and find beauty in something. Note one down each day.

MON:
....
....

TUES:
....
....

WEDS:
....
....

THURS:
....
....

FRI:
....
....

SAT:
....
....

SUN:
....
....

"Work + Time + Belief = Results."

JEFF SHORE

Week Starting : _____

Believe in yourself.
What are your core strengths? Picture yourself being successful.
What are you doing and how are you doing it?

....

....

....

....

....

....

....

....

....

....

....

....

....

....

....

....

....

....

....

"Remember, we all stumble, every one of us. That's why it's a comfort to go hand in hand."

EMILY KIMBROUGH

Week Starting : _____

If you want to be happy, be a friend.
Contact a special friend, arrange to meet up.
Who did you meet and what did you enjoy?

"Physical exercise releases endorphins the 'feel' good hormone."

JAMES A BLUMENTHAL

Week Starting : _____

Review your exercise regime. Is it where you want it to be?
What two things can you do this week that are good for your body?

....
....
....
....
....
....
....

How did you get on? Are there any habits you would like to form and
how can you build these into your life?

....
....
....
....
....
....
....

"You cannot have a positive life and a negative mind."

JOYCE MEYER

Week Starting : _____

How happy will you decide to be this week? It is your choice.
Note down 4 things that you are grateful for.

1.
....
....
....
....

2.
....
....
....
....

3.
....
....
....
....

4.
....
....
....
....

"If someone isn't smiling, give them one of yours."

UNKNOWN

Week Starting : _____

When we are happy we smile and the reverse is also true.
We feel happier and think positive thoughts when we laugh or smile.
Check yourself this week, stop and smile.

....

....

....

....

....

....

....

....

....

....

....

....

....

....

....

....

....

....

....

....

"What would you like to do if you have any free time? Now, be honest and admit how you frequently spend your free time."

PETER COXON

Week Starting : _____

Log some of the things that interest you the
most and that you would like to focus on in your spare time.

....
....
....
....

How could you begin to pursue these interests?

....
....
....
....

What progress did you make?

....
....
....
....
....

"The oak fought the wind and was broken, the willow bent when it must and survived."

ROBERT JORDAN

Imagine yourself as a ball - when you get knocked down be determined to rise above it. Bounce back to the positive, happy and fulfilled person you can be. Write down your 'bounce back ability' moments from the last few months.

....

....

....

....

....

....

....

....

....

....

....

....

....

....

....

....

....

....

....

"Your eyes will process 24 million images in your lifetime. You can smell about 10,000 odours."

ESOMAR CONGRESS

Week Starting : _____

How often do you use all of your senses? This week tune into your
senses and really feel alive to what is around you.
Each day note down one or two senses that made you feel alive.

MON:
....
....

TUES:
....
....

WEDS:
....
....

THURS:
....
....

FRI:
....
....

SAT:
....
....

SUN:
....
....

"Our first and last love is self-love."

CHRISTIAN NESTELL BOVEE

Week Starting : _____

How well are you eating?
What do you want to eat more or less of?
Note down which habit you aim to change this week.

....
....
....
....
....
....
....

Be kind to yourself – what is working well?

....
....
....
....
....
....
....
....

"**Don't just give presents - give yourself.**"

NEIL COXON

Week Starting : _____

What kind of experiences could you arrange to do with your loved ones?

....

....

....

....

....

....

....

What did you arrange and with whom?

....

....

....

....

....

....

....

....

"Inspiration - the process of being mentally stimulated to do or feel something, especially to do something creative."

OXFORD ENGLISH DICTIONARY

Week Starting: _____

Look for an inspiring book. Here's a suggestion - '59 seconds:
think a little, change a lot" by Professor Richard Wiseman.
Make time to read it - what did you learn?

"Is it possible to find peace and quiet in a simpler life? By shedding layers of clutter you can discover more wellbeing."

UNKNOWN

Week Starting : _____

Spring clean your life and de-clutter your world.
Pick one or two of the following or jot down some of your own:

Look in your wardrobe and rid yourself of stuff you don't wear or
want or need. Bag it up and take it to your nearest charity shop.

Look in your garage or shed or wherever you store items you don't
use that often. Do you really need all that stuff? Bag, bin or give
away items you don't use or need.

Clean out your kitchen shelves, throw away anything with an old sell
by date or donate items you simply won't use.

What did you de-clutter?

....

....

....

....

....

....

....

....

....

....

....

"The greatness of a community is most accurately measured by the compassionate actions of its members."

CORETTA SCOTT KING

Week Starting : _____

How could you contribute to your community?
Note down a few activities that you could do and pick
one that you will aim to complete.

....

....

....

....

....

....

....

....

....

....

....

....

....

....

....

....

....

....

"The most rewarding fun comes from taking on a challenge."

JEFF SMITH

Week Starting : _____

Take on a challenge - what could you set yourself to do this week that
would be fun and rewarding for yourself or and/or others?

....

....

....

....

....

....

....

....

....

....

....

....

....

....

....

....

....

....

"You don't need loads of money. Small gifts and acts of kindness can result in surprisingly large and long lasting changes in happiness."

UNKNOWN

This week, cultivate kindness:
Who would you like to show greater kindness to? Note down
ideas for some kind acts you could carry out for these people.

....

....

....

....

....

....

....

....

....

....

....

....

....

....

....

....

....

"Exercise is the key, not only to physical strength, but to peace of mind"

NELSON MANDELA

Select a sport or activity that gets you outside and filling your lungs
with air. At a most simple level, take a walk.
What did you do and love this week?

. . . .

. . . .

. . . .

. . . .

. . . .

. . . .

. . . .

. . . .

. . . .

. . . .

. . . .

. . . .

. . . .

. . . .

. . . .

. . . .

. . . .

"Never get so busy
making a living
that you forget to
make a life."

DOLLY PARTON

Week Starting : _____

Re-look at your life balance, which two aspects of
the wheel do you want to further re-balance?
Write down some key things you can work on this week.

....

....

....

....

....

....

....

....

....

....

....

....

....

....

....

....

....

....

....

....

"There is nothing noble in being superior to your fellow man; true nobility is being superior to your former self."

ERNEST HEMINGWAY

Week Starting : _____

Which vices are you most prone to?

FOOLISHNESS: ☐

INCONSISTENCY: ☐

ANGER: ☐

INJUSTICE: ☐

INFIDELITY: ☐

ENVY: ☐

DESPAIR: ☐

In what way could you combat these vices?

....

....

....

....

....

....

....

....

"Life changes when you stop seeking happiness and decide to be happy."

MARK MANSON

Week Starting : _____

Take a break - find a comfy place and rest.
Think about what is giving you the most joy in your life and dwell
there for a moment or two. Note this down . . .

"The greatest thing you'll ever learn is just to love and be loved in return."

NAT KING COLE

This quote is a reminder to appreciate our loved ones. Choose a loved one or two. What will you say and do this week to show how much you love them?

....

....

....

....

....

....

....

....

....

....

....

....

....

....

....

....

....

....

"Once you replace negative thoughts with positive ones, you'll start having positive results."

WILLIE NELSON

Week Starting : _____

Do something positive each day at home and at work.
Record these thoughts or actions.

MON:
....
....

TUES:
....
....

WEDS:
....
....

THURS:
....
....

FRI:
....
....

SAT:
....
....

SUN:
....
....

THE OXFORD HAPPINESS QUESTIONNAIRE

Re-assessing your own 'set point'

Below are a number of statements about happiness. Using a pencil indicate how much you agree or disagree with each statement by entering a number alongside it according to the scale below.

1	2	3	4	5	6
Strongly disagree	Moderately disagree	Slightly disagree	Slightly agree	Moderately agree	Strongly agree

STATEMENT: SCORE:

1	I don't feel particularly pleased with the way I am	....	R
2	I am intensely interested in other people	....	
3	I feel that life is very rewarding	....	
4	I have very warm feelings towards almost everyone	....	
5	I rarely wake up feeling rested	....	R
6	I'm not particularly optimistic about the future	....	R
7	I find most things amusing	....	

1	2	3	4	5	6
Strongly disagree	Moderately disagree	Slightly disagree	Slightly agree	Moderately agree	Strongly agree

8	I am always committed and involved	....	
9	Life is good	....	
10	I don't think that the world is a good place	....	R
11	I laugh a lot	....	
12	I am well satisfied with everything in my life	....	
13	I don't think I look attractive	....	R
14	There's a gap between what I would like to do and what I have done	....	R
15	I am very happy	....	
16	I find beauty in some things	....	
17	I always have a cheerful effect on others	....	
18	I can find time for everything I want to	....	

1	2	3	4	5	6
Strongly disagree	Moderately disagree	Slightly disagree	Slightly agree	Moderately agree	Strongly agree

19	I feel that I'm not especially in control of my life	R
20	I feel able to take anything on	
21	I feel fully mentally alert	
22.	I often experience joy and elation	
23	I don't find it easy to make decisions	R
24	I don't have a particular sense of meaning and purpose in my life	R
25	I feel I have a great deal of energy	
26	I usually have a positive influence on events	
27	I don't have fun with other people	R
28	I don't feel particularly healthy	R
29	I don't have particularly happy memories of the past	R

HOW TO CALCULATE YOUR SCORE

STEP 1

Your scores on the 12 items marked with an R should be 'reverse-scored' - that is, if you gave yourself a 1, rub it out and change it to a 6; if you gave yourself a 2, change that to a 5; change a 4 to a 3; change a 5 to a 2; and change a 6 to a 1.

STEP 2

Using the changed scores for those 12 items, now add the scores for all the 29 statements.

STEP 3

Happiness 'set point' = Total (from Step 2) divided by 29

Your current happiness 'set point' is:

....

WHAT IT MEANS

Research behind The Oxford Happiness Questionnaire (Hills and Argyle 2002) suggests that we will typically vary no more than +or- 2 points from our 'set point' through life due to events which may raise or lower our 'set point' temporarily, but we are likely to revert to our 'set point' over time.

Your score is 'your score' and can't be compared with others. There is no right or wrong score, but it represents a point in time from which you can move.

How does this score compare to your first result?

....

....

Mid Year Reflections

What has gone well?

....

....

....

....

Best moments to cherish:

....

....

....

....

What has made you joyful?

....

....

....

....

What have you achieved that has made you feel fulfilled?

....

....

....

....

How have you progressed on your work life balance?

....

....

....

....

What joy have you given to others:

....

....

....

....

Looking ahead: What do you imagine for the next 6 months?

....

....

....

....

"If you have good thoughts they will shine out of your face like sunbeams and you will always look lovely."

ROALD DAHL

Energise yourself and your demeanor this week. Walk tall, sit up
straight, relax, swing your arms, put a spring in your step.
Note how people respond to a more energised you.

....

....

....

....

....

....

....

....

....

....

....

....

....

....

....

....

....

....

....

"Don't waste time seeking happiness, spread happiness and your day will be richer."

UNKNOWN

Week Starting : _____

Try the 3:1 positive prescription. Give at least three positive
comments for any negative or challenging comment.
Who would you like to try this with?

....
....
....
....
....
....
....

How did you get on?

....
....
....
....
....
....
....
....

"There's no such thing as bad weather, only unsuitable clothing."

ALFRED WAINWRIGHT

When was the last time you went out for the pure enjoyment of it?
Match the weather with the right clothes and get outside. Go for a
walk or do some gardening - what did you do?

....

....

....

....

....

....

....

....

....

....

....

....

....

....

....

....

....

....

"Everything that is done in the world is done by hope."

MARTIN LUTHER

All life's problems stem from either:
Judgement - of ourselves or of others, Despair or Fear
With this in mind the keys to happiness include:

Forgiveness - Who are you ready to forgive that will
strengthen your own sense of peace and joy?

....

....

....

....

Gratitude - what or who are you grateful for?

....

....

....

....

Hope - what are you hoping for this next few weeks?

....

....

....

....

....

"I realise there's something incredibly honest about trees in winter, how they're experts at letting things go."

JEFFREY MCDANIEL

What frustrations, sadness and/or unnecessary
worries would you like to try letting go of?
Write down 3 things you want to let go and scrub them out.

....

....

....

....

....

....

....

....

....

....

....

....

....

....

....

....

....

....

"Hope and optimism are inspiring."

UNKNOWN

What do you want to learn next and how enthusiastic do you feel
about it? Who or what fills you with hope and optimism?

....

....

....

....

....

....

....

What can you decide to be optimistic about?

....

....

....

....

....

....

....

....

"Reflect upon your present blessings - of which every man has many - not on your past misfortunes, of which all men have some."

CHARLES DICKENS

Sit in front of a mirror and imagine you are meeting yourself through fresh and appreciative eyes. Write down the positive aspects that you notice about this person and their life.

....

....

....

....

....

....

....

....

....

....

....

....

....

....

....

....

....

....

....

....

....

"If you want to conquer the anxiety of life, live in the moment, live in the breath."

AMIT RAY

Week Starting : _____

Meditate - sit in a comfortable chair with your back straight and your
eyes closed. Slowly notice your thoughts subside and become aware
of your in and out breathing. Begin to extend your breaths. Every time
a thought enters your head simply let it go and breath. Start by doing
this for 5 minutes a day in the morning and evening.
Gradually extend the time through the week.

....

....

....

....

....

....

....

....

....

....

....

....

....

....

....

"**Kindness is always fashionable, and always welcome.**"

AMELIA BARR

Week Starting : _____

Everyone loves being complimented, this week go
out of your way to give seven compliments.
What will you say and what did you say to whom?

1.
....
....

2.
....
....

3.
....
....

4.
....
....

5.
....
....

6.
....
....

7.
....
....

"We can turn the pursuit of a meaningful life from a quixotic impossibility to something at which we can all succeed."

ALAIN DE BOTTON

Author Alain de Botton offers a set of 10 virtues for well being:

RESILIENCE
EMPATHY
PATIENCE
SACRIFICE
POLITENESS
HUMOUR
SELF-AWARENESS
FORGIVENESS
HOPE
CONFIDENCE

Which of these are most important to you?

....

....

....

....

....

....

....

....

....

....

....

"Recognising the difference between wants & needs is probably the biggest benefit to conducting a no spend day."

IBID

Week Starting : _____

Organise a no spend day, weekend or week if you can do it. Seek out activities that are free - visit local attractions and events that require no entry fee and take your own food and drink.
Photos are free so you can take lots of them . . .

....
....
....
....
....
....
....
....
....
....
....
....
....
....
....
....
....
....
....
....

"Forget what hurt you but never forget what it taught you."

SHANNON L. ALDER

Write down something you want to let go of. Imagine putting that
thought into a rubbish bag. Now in your mind tie the top and
put it out with the rubbish. Let it go.
Repeat as many times as it takes until it's gone.

"Nothing is more important than thinking thoughts that make you feel good."

ABRAHAM HICKS

Change your thoughts and you can change your world. Think of a
negative situation you have been in.
What is something positive you got out of it?

....

....

....

....

....

....

....

....

....

....

....

....

....

....

....

....

....

....

....

Hope and optimism
are inspiring.

UNKNOWN

Week Starting : _____

How many times a day do you check your social media feeds?
How much of your day does it steal. Be mindful about how, and
when, and how often you use it and how it makes you feel.
Note it down here and adjust as necessary.

"Always look on the
bright side of life."

MONTY PYTHON

Week Starting : _____

List your happy people here.
Note down what they say or do that makes them happy.

. . . .

. . . .

. . . .

. . . .

. . . .

. . . .

. . . .

How do they effect you?

. . . .

. . . .

. . . .

. . . .

. . . .

. . . .

. . . .

. . . .

"Tell me, what is it you plan to do with your one wild and precious life?"

MARY OLIVER

Week Starting : _____

What is the meaning of your life?
Consider why you are here. What difference do you want to make?
What legacy do you wish to leave?

....

....

....

....

....

....

....

What else can you do to pursue your life goals? What's next?

....

....

....

....

....

....

....

....

"We make a living by what we get, but we make a life by what we give."

WINSTON CHURCHILL

Week Starting : _____

Social responsibility means behaving ethically and sensitively
towards social, cultural, economic and environmental issues.
This week organise something that helps your community -
such as a beach, hedge or street clean or a visit or simply
helping an elderly neighbour with the shopping.
What did you do and how did you feel?

....
....
....
....
....
....
....
....
....
....
....
....
....
....
....
....
....
....
....

"Everything that irritates us about others can lead us to an understanding of ourselves."

CARL JUNG

Week Starting : _____

Be honest . . .
What irritates you about others?
Do those things irritate you about yourself?

....
....
....
....

What do you think irritates others about you?

....
....
....
....
....

How can you combat this?

....
....
....
....
....
....

"How do you eat an elephant? One mouthful at a time!"

CREIGHTON ABRAMS

Week Starting : _____

Think of a task you have been putting off completing
and write it down. Now break it into smaller tasks,
list them below and start them one at a time.

1.
....

....

2.
....

....

3.
....

....

4.
....

....

5.
....

....

6.
....

....

7.
....

....

"Laughter is the best medicine, so laugh out loud each day!"

UNKNOWN

Week Starting : _____

Three medicines that don't work:

1. Giving yourself a treat provides a short term boost (at best) and can have longer term negative impact.

2. Isolating yourself when you're blue doesn't help. Go and see your friends.

3. Expressing anger and acting out doesn't get it off your chest - it inflames you more! Instead try remaining quiet and letting it go.

Seek out things that make you laugh . . . and laugh out loud each day.

....

....

....

....

....

....

....

....

....

....

....

....

....

"The less you respond to negative people the more peaceful your life will become."

UNKNOWN

Avoid colluding with negative and cynical thoughts as this is corrosive. Take action this week to turn conversations to the positive, avoid colluding negatively with others or at worst walk away.

....

....

....

....

....

....

....

How did you fair?

....

....

....

....

....

....

....

....

"Proprioceptive psychology research has found we feel happier and think more positively when we smile or nod."

PETER COXON

Week Starting : _____

Try saying 'Yes, and. . .' rather than 'Yes, but. . .'.
If you have a tendency to say no or pause, nod or
smile as an alternative response. How did it go?

....

....

....

....

....

....

....

....

....

....

....

....

....

....

....

....

....

....

....

"Conscious breathing heightens awareness & deepens relaxation."

DAN BRULE

Week Starting : _____

Researchers at the University of Washington found that your accuracy
rates, ability to multi-task and handle stress improved significantly if
each morning you spend two minutes of doing nothing except watch
your breath going in and out and being aware of your surroundings.
Try it this week and note down how it felt for you . .

....

....

....

....

....

....

....

....

....

....

....

....

....

....

....

....

....

....

....

"By avoiding expenses at all costs, we are forced to assess if & why we need to make certain purchases."

MAGGIE MCGRATH

Week Starting : _____

This week seek out alternatives . . .
Only buy what you need and resolve to ignore what you want.
Take your own lunch, snacks and drinks.
Use up items in your cupboard and only use reusable packaging.

....

....

....

....

....

....

....

What savings did you make?

....

....

....

....

....

....

....

....

"You yourself, as much as anybody in the entire universe, deserve your love and affection."

BUDDHA

Week Starting : _____

Plan a date with yourself, what would you really
like to do, when and where? Now book it in.

....
....
....
....
....
....
....
....
....
....
....
....
....
....
....
....
....
....
....

"Using more positively charged emotional words creates an air of happiness."

UNKNOWN

Week Starting : _____

Try using a larger variation in the pitch of your voice and speak slightly faster. Try a firmer handshake, more expressive hand gestures and eye contact. Nod your head more.

Tick which phrases you have said out loud this week . . .

☒ I LOVE . . .

☒ I REALLY LIKE . . .

☒ I'M THRILLED . . .

☒ I'M DELIGHTED . . .

☒ I'VE ENJOYED . . .

☒ I'VE APPRECIATED . . .

☒ I'M GRATEFUL FOR . . .

☒ I'M SO HAPPY . . .

THE OXFORD HAPPINESS QUESTIONNAIRE

Re-assessing your own 'set point'

Below are a number of statements about happiness. Using a pencil indicate how much you agree or disagree with each statement by entering a number alongside it according to the scale below.

1	2	3	4	5	6
Strongly disagree	Moderately disagree	Slightly disagree	Slightly agree	Moderately agree	Strongly agree

STATEMENT: SCORE:

1	I don't feel particularly pleased with the way I am	R
2	I am intensely interested in other people	
3	I feel that life is very rewarding	
4	I have very warm feelings towards almost everyone	
5	I rarely wake up feeling rested	R
6	I'm not particularly optimistic about the future	R
7	I find most things amusing	

1	2	3	4	5	6
Strongly disagree	Moderately disagree	Slightly disagree	Slightly agree	Moderately agree	Strongly agree

8	I am always committed and involved	....	
9	Life is good	....	
10	I don't think that the world is a good place	....	R
11	I laugh a lot	....	
12	I am well satisfied with everything in my life	....	
13	I don't think I look attractive	....	R
14	There's a gap between what I would like to do and what I have done	....	R
15	I am very happy	....	
16	I find beauty in some things	....	
17	I always have a cheerful effect on others	....	
18	I can find time for everything I want to	....	

1	2	3	4	5	6
Strongly disagree	Moderately disagree	Slightly disagree	Slightly agree	Moderately agree	Strongly agree

19	I feel that I'm not especially in control of my life	....	R
20	I feel able to take anything on	....	
21	I feel fully mentally alert	....	
22.	I often experience joy and elation	....	
23	I don't find it easy to make decisions	....	R
24	I don't have a particular sense of meaning and purpose in my life	....	R
25	I feel I have a great deal of energy	....	
26	I usually have a positive influence on events	....	
27	I don't have fun with other people	....	R
28	I don't feel particularly healthy	....	R
29	I don't have particularly happy memories of the past	....	R

HOW TO CALCULATE YOUR SCORE

STEP 1

Your scores on the 12 items marked with an R should be 'reverse-scored' - that is, if you gave yourself a 1, rub it out and change it to a 6; if you gave yourself a 2, change that to a 5; change a 4 to a 3; change a 5 to a 2; and change a 6 to a 1.

STEP 2

Using the changed scores for those 12 items, now add the scores for all the 29 statements.

STEP 3

Happiness 'set point' = Total (from Step 2) divided by 29

Your current happiness 'set point' is:

....

WHAT IT MEANS

Research behind The Oxford Happiness Questionnaire (Hills and Argyle 2002) suggests that we will typically vary no more than +or– 2 points from our 'set point' through life due to events which may raise or lower our 'set point' temporarily, but we are likely to revert to our 'set point' over time.

Your score is 'your score' and can't be compared with others. There is no right or wrong score, but it represents a point in time from which you can move.

How does this score compare to your first and second result?

....

....

Year End Reflections

What has gone well?

....

....

....

....

Best moments to cherish:

....

....

....

....

What has made you joyful?

....

....

....

....

What have you achieved that has made you feel fulfilled?

....
....
....
....

How have you progressed on your work life balance?

....
....
....
....

What joy have you given to others:

....
....
....
....

Looking ahead: What do you imagine next?

....
....
....
....

Forward Thinking
A WELLBEING, HAPPINESS & FULFILMENT JOURNAL

Author : Peter Coxon who can be contacted at **www.optleadership.com**

The Mindful Collection, first published by Journals Of A Lifetime,
an imprint of from you to me ltd, in August 2018

made with love *from you to me*
www.JournalsOfALifetime.com

There are three titles in the collection:
Forward Thinking, This Is Me & Wonderful Days

To personalise journals and books as well as purchase
other products produced by us, please go to

www.JournalsOfALifetime.com

Printed and bound in China.
This paper is manufactured from pulp sourced from
forests that are legally and sustainably managed.

from you to me, The Old Brewery, Newtown, Bradford on Avon, BA15 1NF, UK

ISBN 978-1-907860-26-3

A JOURNAL OF A LIFETIME